The Small Miracle

Paul Gallico's

The Small Miracle

A Story of Faith and Love

Adapted from the Hallmark Hall of Fame
television presentation, starring

Vittorio De Sica *as Father Damico*
Raf Vallone *as Father Superior*
Marco Della Cava *as Pepino*

Photographs by Jack Jonathan

Story Adaptation by Edward Cunningham

HALLMARK ♛ CROWN EDITIONS

The publishers gratefully acknowledge the contributions of those who brought *The Small Miracle* to the television screen and made this volume possible: John Patrick and Arthur Dales, who collaborated on the script; Jeannot Szwarc, who served as director; Duane C. Bogie, producer, FCB Productions; and Alan Landsburg, executive producer, Alan Landsburg Productions.

The Small Miracle

NOT SO FAR FROM ROME, there is a colorful little town called Assisi. It lies at the foot of Mt. Subasio, overlooking the beautiful Umbrian Valley. Each year thousands of people from all parts of the world come to Assisi to visit the famous Church of St. Francis, which is the last resting place of the Great Saint who founded it in the twelfth century.

Many stories have been told about St. Francis and the spirit of innocent faith and unselfish love that was his legacy. One of the most beautiful concerns a small boy named PEPINO, his donkey VIOLETTA and FATHER DAMICO, the kind old Franciscan priest who loved them both.

Pepino was a bright, energetic boy who lived with his grandfather. They were very poor, and Pepino had to work hard to support their little home. That is why he felt so lucky to have a fine, strong helper like Violetta. Every day they would go to the marketplace to carry water, haul luggage for tourists, show people around the city — anything to make some money.

Pepino was always proud when someone asked to have souvenir pictures taken with Violetta in front of the big church. For a few pennies he would put a flowery hat on Violetta's head and coax her to smile for the camera. Smiling came easy for Violetta since she loved posing, especially with children.

Pepino's best friend — next to Violetta — was Father Damico.
He watched over the boy like a guardian angel
and tried to help whenever he could.
Pepino loved to hear Father Damico's stories about
St. Francis, who had always been so kind and generous
to people and, best of all, to animals like Violetta.
Sometimes, as Pepino listened to

Father Damico, he imagined he was hearing the voice of the Gentle Saint himself. In time Pepino developed a strong faith in St. Francis. Indeed, whenever he needed special help, St. Francis was the first to hear about it. The boy's prayers were mostly for small things, like a little extra money to buy a sack of figs for his grandfather's birthday. But then one day Violetta got sick, and Pepino found himself in need of a small miracle.

When Pepino went to the stable that morning, Violetta had disappeared. Almost in tears, he ran to tell Father Damico. They searched the countryside and finally, towards evening, they found Violetta lying on her side near the river. Together they helped her back to the stable.

The doctor came and gave Violetta a big pill, saying that all they could do was watch her closely for the next few days and hope for the best. Father Damico promised he would pray to St. Francis for Violetta's recovery and urged Pepino to do the same. For three days the heartsick boy stayed by his donkey's side and waited…and watched …and prayed.

When Violetta's condition did not improve, Pepino came to Father Damico with an idea. He wanted to take Violetta down to the tomb of St. Francis beneath the church. He told of the time his friend Gianni had taken a sick mouse there, and when St. Francis saw how the little creature was suffering he helped it get well right away. Surely he would do the same for a donkey.

Father Damico shook his head sadly and said that Violetta was much too big to be taken down the narrow steps of the crypt. Besides that, Father Superior had strictly forbidden animals in the church.

But Pepino remembered hearing about a lower entrance to the crypt that had been walled up for years. How simple it would be, he suggested, to knock out a few bricks so that Violetta could get through. All they needed was Father Superior's permission.

Reluctantly Father Damico agreed to take Pepino to see Father Superior.

Father Superior was perched high on a ladder in the library when Pepino entered. He listened to the boy's request, but firmly refused to consider tearing down a church wall for a donkey. The answer was an emphatic "No!"

Afterwards Father Damico tried to comfort Pepino.

"Father Superior is a very wise man," the old priest said. "We must try to accept his judgment."

"But is there no one wiser than Father Superior?" the boy asked.

After considering the question for a moment, Father Damico replied, "The higher one goes in the church, the wiser one must be. Therefore the Pope must be the wisest of us all."

"That settles it," said Pepino.

"I shall go to see the Pope!"

Father Damico began to feel really troubled. He tried his best to explain that Violetta's life was in God's hands and that not even the Holy Father could change that. But Pepino wouldn't listen. He was determined to leave for Rome at sunrise.

"But this is impossible," Father Superior said angrily when Father Damico explained Pepino's plan. "Tell the boy he cannot go."

"I have tried," said Father Damico with a shrug. "But sometimes Pepino is more stubborn than his donkey. You see — Violetta is all he has in the world, and he would do anything to save her."

"This is all your fault," Father Superior accused. "It was you who taught him to believe that St. Francis could always work miracles, and it was you who planted this ridiculous idea of seeing the Pope in his head. Now, if the donkey dies, he will hold you responsible."

"Yes, I know," the old priest admitted sadly. "But please — let me go with Pepino. It will give me a chance to reason with him some more. Maybe I can still persuade him to resign himself to the Lord's will."

Father Superior deliberated for a moment. Perhaps it *would* be good for the boy to be away for a few days, he thought. It might take his mind off the animal's suffering. "Very well," he said wearily. "You may go along. But I shall expect you back in two days. And after this, no more nonsense!"

And so, at the break of dawn, a confident Pepino
and a worried Father Damico were on their way to Rome.

They planned to hike ten miles to the main highway and then catch a ride into the great city. Father Damico hadn't walked so far in ages. He found it hard to keep up with his young friend. Between puffs he spoke of St. Francis' faith in God's providence and how it applied to Violetta's illness. He said that if God decided to take Violetta, Pepino must be prepared to accept His will. Then he began to question whether going to Rome was the wisest thing for them to do. Pepino listened to everything he said, but never once slowed down.

In time they came upon a beautiful stream and couldn't resist the temptation to go for a swim before lunch. Splashing and frolicking in the cool water, they didn't observe the man who crept out of the bushes to steal their food and, worse yet, Father Damico's robe.

"This is awful!" cried Father Damico, secretly pleased to have an excuse to return to Assisi. "How can I go to Rome now?"

Pepino picked up the tattered clothes the thief had left. "You'll just have to wear these," he said with a mischievous smile. "Surely this is a sign that St. Francis is watching over us."

"But Pepino," the old priest cried, "what kind of a sign would steal our clothes, our food and all of our money?"

"Don't you see?" said Pepino. "Now you're just like St. Francis. Remember the story of his pilgrimage to Rome? Who knows — maybe he stopped in this very place. And don't you remember how he gave his clothes to poor people he met along the way? I'm sure he'd be very proud of you right now."

As he put on the thief's clothes, Father Damico pictured himself in the role of St. Francis. Perhaps the boy is right, he thought. This is indeed the same route the Blessed Saint took to Rome. Maybe it is the Lord's will that Pepino and I should follow in his footsteps. Father Superior will be very angry with me, but maybe God will be very happy.

After they reached the highway, it seemed forever until a truck finally stopped. At first the truck driver, a big rough-looking man, was quite suspicious. He didn't believe Father Damico was really a priest, and he laughed and shook his head when Pepino explained the reason for their journey. Then, after a few silent miles, he and Pepino struck up a friendly conversation. He even shared his bread and sausage when he learned they hadn't eaten all day.

"See, Father Damico," Pepino whispered, "St. Francis is taking care of us."

The old priest smiled, touched by the unexpected generosity of a truck driver and the unquestioning faith of a ten-year-old boy.

The truck driver took them as far as the Rome-Pescara intersection, where they spent the night.

Early next morning they hitched another ride with a man named Mr. Mangione, who seemed helpful and considerate…at first. He was a tombstone salesman, and the back of his fancy convertible was loaded with heavy monuments and small, expensive statues. Mr. Mangione explained that he needed to make a few stops along the way, but promised they would be in Rome before the day was over.

They stopped at five different cemeteries. Each time, Pepino and Father Damico were asked to unload a tombstone. They pitched in eagerly to show appreciation for the ride, but it was hard work and, as the hours passed, they grew very tired and hungry. The salesman made no effort at all to help them.

At noon he decided to have lunch. His two weary helpers watched as he finished off an enormous sausage, a large wedge of cheese, half a loaf of bread and a whole bottle of wine. Of course he didn't offer them a single bite. When he was finished, he announced that he was late for a meeting back in Pescara, apologized for not completing the trip to Rome and prepared to leave.

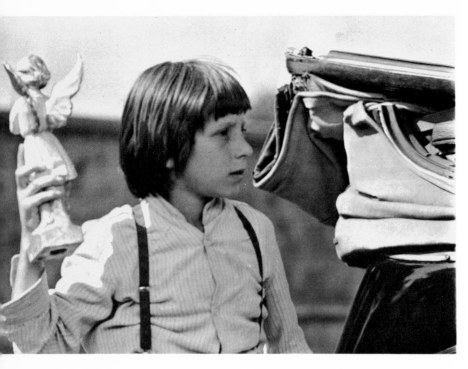

The thought of Violetta lying sick in her stable flashed across Pepino's mind. I will not be tricked that easily, he thought. Desperately, he snatched one of the statues from the back seat of the car, held it high above his head and threatened to smash it to bits unless Mr. Mangione took them straight to Rome.

"You little monster," the salesman screamed. "If anything happens to that statue, I'll see that you both go to jail!" As he started after Pepino, the statue slipped from the boy's hand and shattered on the road.

Mr. Mangione may not have been good at keeping promises, but he certainly followed through on his threats. Within the hour Pepino and Father Damico were in the Pescara jailhouse.

What else can go wrong, wondered Pepino, thinking back over his misfortunes. Violetta is depending on me for help, and here I am behind bars. Exhausted by the

day's activities, he fell asleep in the middle of a prayer to St. Francis.

The two prisoners were awakened next morning by the angry voice of Father Superior, who had been summoned by the local police.

"I might have known this little adventure would come to no good," cried the angry priest. "What a fool I was to allow you two children to leave Assisi. Come, get in the car. We are going back home at once!"

On their way back toward Assisi, Father Superior accused Father Damico of being an irresponsible dreamer and chided Pepino for his lack of faith in prayer.

"But you don't understand," the boy said. "I want to pray very much. The trouble is you won't let me take Violetta to pray at the tomb of St. Francis."

"Indeed I won't," snapped Father Superior. "You can pray just as effectively anywhere." And he began to drive a little faster.

That gave Pepino another idea. Suddenly he asked if they could stop and have something to eat. They entered a busy roadside restaurant and, as the two priests sat down at a table, Pepino fell to his knees, clasped his hands and began to pray very loudly.

"Dear Lord, Father Superior says I can pray anyplace, so I will pray right here. My name is Pepino and my donkey Violetta is very sick and if I don't get to Rome she may die. Please make Father Superior take pity on poor Violetta and allow me to go to Rome."

By this time Pepino was the center of attention. Everyone in the restaurant was listening to his prayer. The louder he prayed, the more embarrassed Father Superior became.

"Pepino, we are going to eat now," said Father Damico. "What would you like to order?"

"Lasagna," the boy replied, and kept right on praying. "Please, Lord, make Father Superior listen to me. Tell him it will be all right if I continue my journey to Rome."

The boy continued praying all through the meal until Father Superior's patience was at the breaking point. "All right, all right," he said as they left the restaurant, "go to Rome!"

"Me too?" asked Father Damico.

"Yes, you too. Both of you. Go to Rome. Go anywhere. But leave me in peace."

"Amen," said Pepino.

With high hopes
the two travelers set out once more.
Before long they had found another ride
and, later that same day,
they arrived in the eternal city of Rome.

Neither of them had ever seen so many buildings…or so many people!

"So beautiful!" said Father Damico.

"So big!" said Pepino.

But the scene was too awesome for words and, for a while, they felt lost in the surging traffic and milling crowds of the gigantic city. At last Pepino spotted the majestic dome of St. Peter's, and off they hurried in that direction.

They lingered a moment in front of the fountain in the Piazza San Pietro, stunned and a little bit scared to find themselves in the center of such magnificence. If only Violetta could be here to see all this, Pepino thought. Then, remembering their mission, he tugged impatiently at Father Damico's sleeve.

As they walked down the long colonnade of the entrance to the Vatican, doubts began once more to form in Father Damico's mind. Grasping Pepino's arm, he said, "Maybe we have been fooling ourselves, my son. Do you really believe the Holy Father will have time to talk about a donkey? Let's turn back."

"We've come this far, haven't we?" replied Pepino. "Don't worry, St. Francis is on our side." And he ran toward the Swiss guard who stood before the main doorway. Father Damico followed slowly, afraid that even the great St. Francis couldn't get them through this door.

"Excuse me. Is the Pope in?" Pepino asked. Then he explained his problem.

"If you don't have an appointment, you can't see the Pope," said the amused guard. "First you must write a letter of application."

"Oh, I see," said Pepino cheerfully. "Please stay here a minute. I will write a note and you can give it to the Pope while I wait."

The guard looked at Father Damico and winked.

Father Damico knew he must do something to save Pepino from further disappointment. He told the boy to wait while he found a member of his order and got some advice.

Pepino, however, was too excited to wait. He ran back out to the Piazza and asked an old lady who was selling flowers for paper and pencil, explaining that he had to write a letter to the Pope to save his donkey's life. She watched smiling as he wrote:

Dear Holy Father,

I am Pepino. I am ten years old and come from the town of Assisi. I need to talk to you about something very important. If I don't see you, my donkey will die. Please help me. I'll be waiting right out in front of your house.

Your Friend, Pepino

The kind lady gave him a small bouquet of flowers to put with his letter, and he hurried back to the guard.

"Please deliver this for me. It's very urgent," he said.

"I'll be off duty soon," said the guard, humoring him. "I'll be sure to deliver it then." With that, he put the bouquet and letter on a little table just inside the door and promptly forgot about them.

Pepino walked around the Piazza for nearly fifteen minutes. When he returned, there was a new guard, but his bouquet and letter were still on the table.

"He forgot my letter!" Pepino cried.

"Who forgot what?" the new guard asked.

"The other guard was going to deliver that letter to the Pope."

"No one takes letters to the Pope," replied the guard, shaking his head sternly.

"But you don't understand," insisted Pepino. "The Holy Father must read my letter. My donkey is sick, and he can help her."

"Be on your way," the guard threatened, "before I call a policeman."

Then, almost without thinking, Pepino darted under the guard's arm and through the door. Grabbing the bouquet and letter, he sped down the corridor as the astonished guard began to chase him, shouting, "You! Little boy! Come back here!"

Through the building Pepino scrambled, dodging this way and that, completely lost in the maze of hallways. Finally three guards cornered him and, during the struggle that followed, the letter and flowers fell from his grasp.

He was being escorted out the door as Father Damico returned. The priest had found a Franciscan monastery nearby where he received a shave and a new robe. But no one there could tell him how to arrange an impromptu audience with the Pope.

How stupid I have been, Father Damico thought when he saw the dejected boy. How could I have built up his hopes, knowing what a bitter disappointment lay in store. Father Superior is right in thinking I am an irresponsible dreamer. He rushed over to console the heartbroken Pepino.

Meanwhile, inside, a curious thing was happening. Moments after Pepino's capture, Sister Claudia, who worked in the library, had discovered his bouquet and letter on the floor. She was so moved by the boy's words that she showed the letter to Monsignor Barelli, who took it immediately to Cardinal Simone, the Pope's personal assistant.

Pepino, of course, knew nothing of this. He had given up all hope. "Violetta will die," he sobbed. "What good are all my prayers? Nobody cares. Nobody will help me."

"Please don't think that," Father Damico pleaded. "It was all my fault. I should never have encouraged you to come here. Please forgive me for misleading you so."

They sat for a while in the Piazza, so lost in their grief that they didn't even notice Cardinal Simone walking toward them. Pepino's eyes widened in disbelief when he heard the Cardinal call his name. He nodded uncertainly when asked if he were the boy who had written the letter. Then, taking his hand, the smiling Cardinal led him back up the stairs and into the Vatican, while Father Damico watched in wonderment.

Pepino was whisked down a long,
beautifully decorated corridor,
through a grand hall,
and up to the door of the Pope's office.

"Please go in,"
said Cardinal Simone.
"The Holy Father
is expecting you."

Exactly what Pepino said to the Pope or what the Pope said to Pepino was never disclosed. But the news of their visit had already reached Assisi when the travelers arrived home in a shiny black limousine flying the Vatican flag. There was great excitement when Pepino leaped from the car waving a note the Pope had given him.

When people began to question him about the contents of the note, Pepino only smiled a mysterious little smile, handed it to Father Damico to deliver to Father Superior and dashed off to see his beloved Violetta.

When Pepino reached the stable, Violetta seemed in worse condition than ever. He threw himself on the ground by her side and embraced her. "Violetta," he whispered, "you are going to get well. The Holy Father himself has written a note to open the wall for you. You are going with me right now to the tomb of St. Francis. Do you hear? St. Francis is going to help you get well!"

With great effort he helped Violetta to her feet, and slowly they walked back to town. Father Damico and Father Superior met them at the lower wall where stone-masons were already lifting out some large stones to make an entrance.

Once again Father Damico tried to prepare Pepino for the worst. "There's one thing you must remember before you take Violetta into the crypt," the old priest warned. "St. Francis may wish to have your donkey with him in heaven. He loved animals, and Violetta is very beautiful. If this happens, you must be prepared to give as well as receive."

Pepino had never considered that St. Francis might want Violetta for himself. "No!" he cried. "St. Francis doesn't need Violetta. He has God."

Patiently Father Damico explained that Pepino also had God, that indeed God had been very close to him these past several days. He reminded the boy that it was up to God to decide whether or not Violetta would get well, and that they could only abide by His will. "Now tell me, my son," Father Damico asked gently, "if St. Francis wants Violetta, would you give her to him?"

Pepino thought a few moments longer, then nodded his head sadly. "Yes," he said, blinking back a tear, "but I sure wouldn't want to."

Just then, one of the stonemasons ran up to Father Superior with a small, dusty iron box. "I found this embedded in the wall, Father," the man said, handing him the box. The two priests looked at each other in amazement.

"Is it possible?" wondered Father Superior aloud.

"There can't be any doubt," said Father Damico. "See…it's inscribed. It belonged to St. Francis."

Slowly, with trembling hands, Father Superior opened the box. Inside they found a feather, a dried flower and a few seeds.

"But what can it mean?" asked Father Superior.

"Don't you see?" said Father Damico. "These are the things St. Francis loved. He has left us memories of a skylark, a wild primrose and wheat that feeds the hungry. What better symbols could there be of the beauty and bounty of God's earth?"

"It is a miracle!" exclaimed Father Superior.

"Praise be to God!" exclaimed Father Damico.

And the priests watched as Pepino led Violetta past them toward the light of the open crypt.

"Thank you, St. Francis," Father Damico prayed as the brave boy and his donkey disappeared into the welcoming glow. "Thank you for this day of small miracles."

—THE END—

The Prayer of St. Francis of Assisi

LORD,

make me an instrument of Thy peace:

Where there is hatred, let me sow love.

Where there is injury, pardon.

Where there is doubt, faith.

Where there is despair, hope.

Where there is darkness, light.

Where there is sadness, joy.

O Divine Master, grant that I may not so much

Seek to be consoled, as to console;

To be understood, as to understand;

To be loved, as to love.

For it is in giving that we receive,

It is in pardoning that we are pardoned,

And it is in dying that we are born to Eternal Life.

Set in Trump Mediaeval,
a classic Roman and Italic created by Georg Trump.
The calligraphic Uncial used through this book
was created exclusively for Hallmark by Hermann Zapf.
Printed on Hallmark Crown Royale Book paper.
Book design by Susan Peter.